Suddenly the light fell on something.
Long silver beams. Then Shap saw the web.

"Look at this," he said.

"We're stuck in a big net," said Lin.

"It's a web," said Shap.

Starhunter was trapped in a massive web.
It hung between the mountains. The starship
had flown right into it.

"Who put a web here?" said Lin.

"A spider. A monster spider," said Rikk.
"And here it comes!"

The crew looked across to a cave in the
mountains. A monster spider had come out.
It crawled along the web towards them.
Its metal fangs flashed in the light.

Zero Zone III
The Web

David Walke

1 ARAK

The Starship crashed to a stop. The crew smashed onto the deck. Rikk pulled himself up. He grabbed the controls. He put the engines on full blast. The ship shook but it did not move. It was stuck. Something had trapped Starhunter.

"What's going on?" said Shap.

"The ship won't move," said Lin.

"Something has got us. We're trapped!" said Rikk.

Shap looked out of the cabin window. The ship had been flying over mountains on the planet Arak. They were on the way to Sen Tak to meet Queen Sen. The ship had suddenly crashed to a stop.

Shap could see nothing out of the window. Starhunter was stuck in midair. There were high mountains all around. The ship hung between them.

2 SPIDERS

"Let's get out of here!" yelled Shap. He ran to the controls.

"Blast the engines! Go! Go!" cried Rikk.

"It's no good. We're still stuck!" called Lin.

"OP2, fire the cannons!" cried Rikk.

OP2 pushed the cannon controls. Nothing happened. The cannons were stuck in the web. Rikk looked outside. The massive metal spider crawled slowly along the web. It was coming to get them. They had to get loose.

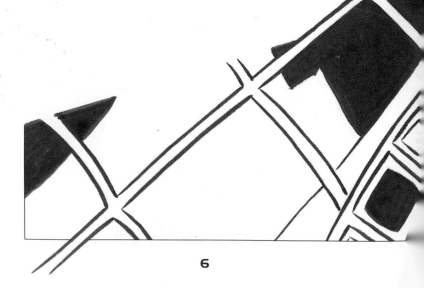

Rikk grabbed a jetpack and put it on.
He took a gun from the rack. He ran to the
hatch. It slid open and he fired the jetpack.
He went up through the hatch. He could see
the mass of silver web around Starhunter.
The monster spider kept on coming.

Rikk got his gun and fired. Sparks flew up
as bits of the web shattered. He fired again.
More web smashed but the ship was still
stuck. The spider was getting closer.
Two more spiders came out of the rocks.
They began to crawl along the web.

"Look out, Captain. There are more spiders!"
yelled Shap.

"OP2, can you fire the cannons yet?" cried Lin.

"No. They are still trapped in the web,"
said OP2.

"I'll try blasting them with my gun," said Rikk.

He spun round and fired at the first
monster. The shot smashed into its metal
legs. The spider screamed and stopped.
Rikk fired at the web again. Silver sparks
flew up round the ship. Rikk turned back
to the spider. It was coming at him again.

"We've got to get out of here or we've
had it," he yelled.

"Try blasting the engines again," said Shap.

"I'm going to spin the ship. It might snap
the web," said Lin.

"Hurry up. This thing's coming for me!"
said Rikk.

3 OUT

Lin hit the controls. There was a blast from the engines. The ship began to spin.
It dragged the web with it. Suddenly the web snapped. There was a hole. Starhunter blasted through it.

"Hey! Come back!" yelled Rikk. He shot at the spider again.

"Hang on, Captain!" said Lin.

"Hurry! The spider's going to get him," cried Shap.

"The cannons are OK now. Ready to fire," said OP2.

Starhunter swooped round and flew back to the web. Rikk kept shooting at the spiders. OP2 blasted the cannons at them.

"We have to get the Captain!" said Lin.

"How are we going to get back through the web?" said Shap.

"We made a hole. I'm going through it," said Lin.

"It's too small. We'll never make it," said Shap.

"Yes we will!" said Lin and she went for the hole.

The first spider opened its fangs. Rikk put a
shot into them. Starhunter zoomed through
the hole and came up behind him. He fired
his jetpack and dropped through the hatch.
The spiders screamed as the ship blasted past.

"Go! Go! Go! Let's get out of here!"
yelled Rikk.

4 SEN TAK

Starhunter swooped up and away from Arak. The Starship turned for Sen Tak. Queen Sen had asked the crew to help.

"Why does the Queen need help?" asked Shap.

"I don't know," said Rikk.

"I hope she's not in danger," said Lin.

"It's OK. If she is in danger, we can sort it out," said Rikk.

Starhunter flew over the Queen's palace.
It landed by the gates. The crew stepped
out of the ship. They looked up at the tall
black towers. It all seemed fine. Rikk took
his gun and slipped it into his belt.

"Just in case," he said.

Then he went up to the gates.

5 QUEEN SEN

The massive palace gates slowly opened.
Rikk, Lin and Shap went inside. They were
in a long hall. It was dark. At the far end
were two high doors. They swung open.

The crew saw a room filled with gold light.
A figure stood on a high platform. It was the
Queen. She was waiting for them.

"Queen Sen, we are the crew of Starhunter,"
said Rikk.

"You asked for our help," said Shap.

"Are you in danger?" asked Lin.

The Queen looked down at them.

"I am in no danger," she said. "I do not
need your help."

Rikk looked around him. This did not feel good. It did not seem right. He felt for his gun. He looked up at the figure. Was this Queen Sen?

"Let's get out of here!" said Rikk.

"What's going on?" Shap asked.

"It's a trap!" said Rikk "This is not Queen Sen!"

"Stop! You are my prisoners!" said the figure.

Guards ran down the hall. Rikk pulled out his gun and fired. Shap and Lin ran to the door. The guards fired at them. Shots smashed off the walls. Shap pulled at the doors. They were locked.

A guard grabbed Lin. Rikk spun round
and fired his gun. The guard fell back.
Shap grabbed his gun. He fired at the
Queen's men. They fired back.
Shots crashed into the door beside him.

"There are too many of them!" yelled Shap.

"Can we get out?" called Rikk.

"No! The doors are locked! We're trapped!"
cried Shap.

There was a scream. Rikk and Shap looked round. The guards had got Lin.
They dragged her to the platform.
Rikk and Shap stopped firing.

"I am Han. Give up or you will never see this girl again," said the figure.

Rikk and Shap dropped their guns.

6 THE TOWER

"I am Han," said the figure. "I am Queen of Tak now. Put them in the tower."

The guards dragged the crew through the palace. They climbed high up the tower steps. They threw them into a dark damp room. The door slammed shut behind them.

Shap kicked at the door. It was solid.
He ran to the window. It was too narrow
to get out. He could see Starhunter on the
ground far below. He went back across the
room to Rikk and Lin.

"We've got to get out of here," said Shap.

"The door is locked and we're a long way up.
How do we do it?" asked Lin.

"Shhh!" said Rikk. He put his finger to his lips.

"What is it?" said Shap.

"Listen!" said Rikk.

They could see nothing but they could hear
a sound.

They looked around the tower room.
There was nothing. Then they heard it.
A soft sound. It was the sound of someone
crying. Rikk went slowly down the room.
It was dark but he could see a small shape.

There was a pile of rags in the corner.
Rikk went to it. He lifted a black cloth.
There was someone hiding there. A young
girl looked up at him. Tears ran down
her face.

"Who are you?" said Rikk.

"I am Queen Sen," said the girl.
"Please help me."

7 SECRET

Lin ran to the young Queen. She held her hand.

"What has happened here?" asked Lin.

"Han was my friend. Now she is my enemy. She wants this planet," said the girl.

"Don't worry. You will be Queen again," said Rikk.

"We've got to get her out of here first," said Shap.

Rikk went to the door. He hit it. It was solid. He looked around the walls. There was no way out. He went to the window. He could see Starhunter far below. Was OP2 still down there? Had the guards got him?

"There is a way out," said the Queen.

Rikk turned to her. She told them of a secret passage.

The passage was in the walls of the tower. It went down to a tunnel. The tunnel led to a secret door out of the palace.

"But we have to get out of that door first," said the Queen.

Rikk bent down and felt for his boot.
A small button was hidden on the side.
He pushed it. Then he waited. Far below
a light flashed on OP2. The little robot
came out from his hiding place.
The guards had not found him.

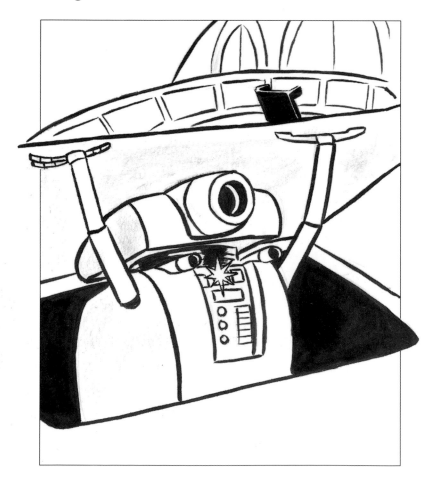

Rikk went to the narrow window. OP2 flew
up to meet him. He had got guns for the crew.
Rikk took them in through the window.
He gave them to Shap and Lin.

"Get rid of this door, OP2," said Rikk.

OP2 could see the door through the window.
He aimed his laser. Then he fired. The laser
beam hit the door. There was a bang and it
smashed open.

8 PASSAGE

"OK. Let's go!" yelled Rikk.

He jumped through the door. Shap, Lin and Queen Sen came after him. Two guards ran up the tower steps. They pulled out their guns and fired at Rikk.

Shots slammed into the wall. Rikk fired back. His shots sent sparks flying up in the air. The guards jumped out of the way. More guards came. Shots smashed into the walls around the crew.

"Where's the secret passage?" yelled Shap.

He ducked as a shot just missed him. Queen Sen ran to the wall. She pushed a stone. The wall slid open. There was a passage with steps down. Lin and Queen Sen stepped inside. Rikk and Shap kept on shooting.

"Come on!" cried Lin.

Rikk and Shap jumped into the passage.
The guards tried to get them. The wall slid
shut. There were loud bangs as the guards
blasted into the wall. The crew and the
Queen ran down the steps.

The passage twisted down and down.
They kept on running. There was a crash
as the guards smashed through the wall.

"Go! Go! Fast!" yelled Rikk.

He turned and sent a shot up the passage.
The guards ducked. One fell and rolled
over and over down the steps.

Suddenly the crew got to the bottom.
The passage stopped. There was a tunnel to
a small metal door in the wall. Shap pushed it.
It did not open. He kicked it with his foot.
The door was jammed.

"What do we do now?" he yelled.

The guards came running down the steps.
They were shooting. Rikk looked at the guards.
Then at the door. It was shut. It was jammed.
There was no way out.

9 ESCAPE

Shots smashed into the wall. Shap ducked.
Lin put her arm around the Queen.
Shap fired back. Rikk dropped down behind
him and shot fast. He felt for his boot.
He pushed the button.

"Get back! Get back to the wall!" yelled Rikk.

BANG! CRASH!

OP2 hit the other side of the door with his laser. The door blew in.

"Come on! Lets go!" yelled Rikk.

They jumped through the door and ran across to Starhunter. OP2 had the engines running. Guards ran out of the palace firing at them. Shots hit the ground all around.

They got to the starship. Rikk slipped into his seat. He slammed the controls. Starhunter blasted off. Shap fired the cannons. Blasts hit the walls of the palace.

Starhunter pulled up and away. The engines screamed. Lin looked back at the palace. The massive gates opened. A red starfighter slid out. Four black fighters came after it. Then more and more came out. The sky was full of fighters coming after Starhunter.

"Look out, Captain! Fighters are after us!" cried Lin.

"It is Han. She wants me," said the Queen.

"Lin! Full blast!" said Rikk.

"Cannons set to fire, Captain!" said OP2.

Han was in the red fighter. She was in the lead.
The others followed as she went into the
attack. Rikk spun Starhunter over as shells
crashed around them. OP2 fired the cannon.
There was a flash of flame. A black fighter
smashed into a ball of fire.

Han kept on coming. Rikk checked his screen.
There were fighters behind and above them.
He pulled Starhunter up to try and get away.
The fighters still came after them. A shell
smashed into the side of the ship.
Starhunter rocked.

The Queen screamed.

"It's no good. I must give myself up," she cried.

"Starhunter does not give up," said Rikk.

"The fighters have got us like rats in
a trap!" cried Lin.

A trap!

Rikk had an idea!

10 TRAP

Rikk pulled Starhunter round.

"Where are we going?" yelled Shap.

"Arak!" said Rikk.

Starhunter skimmed across the sky. Han and
her fighters came after them. They kept on
firing. Rikk twisted and turned the
starship. Shells blew up around
them. He could see Arak ahead.

"That's Arak!" yelled Shap.

"What about the web?" cried Lin.

"I'm going to take a chance!"
said Rikk.

Then they saw it. The web. Rikk went to fly over it. Then Starhunter dropped down. Rikk went right for the silver beams. The fighters came after him. Rikk flew full blast at the web.

"We're going to hit it!" yelled Shap.

"We'll crash into it!" cried Lin.

Then Rikk saw the hole. It was the hole Starhunter had made. He went for it.
The starship screamed through. The fighters tried to follow. The hole was too small.
It was too late for them to turn back.

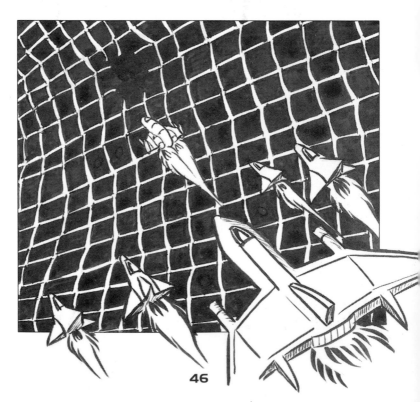

"Aah!" cried Han as her fighter smashed into the web.

The other fighters followed. They smashed and crashed into the web. They were stuck fast. They tried to get out but they were trapped.

Then the spiders began to crawl along the web. The crew watched as their metal jaws sank into the fighters.

"No! No! No!" screamed Han.

11 END

Queen Sen lifted her head and smiled.
She stood on the platform in the palace hall.

"My planet must thank the crew of Starhunter.
You have saved us. You are brave people.
Thank you," she said.

The crew waved. Then Rikk turned and led
them out to Starhunter. The ship lifted off.
Then it blasted across the sky,
deep into the Zero Zone.

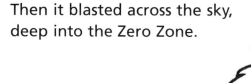